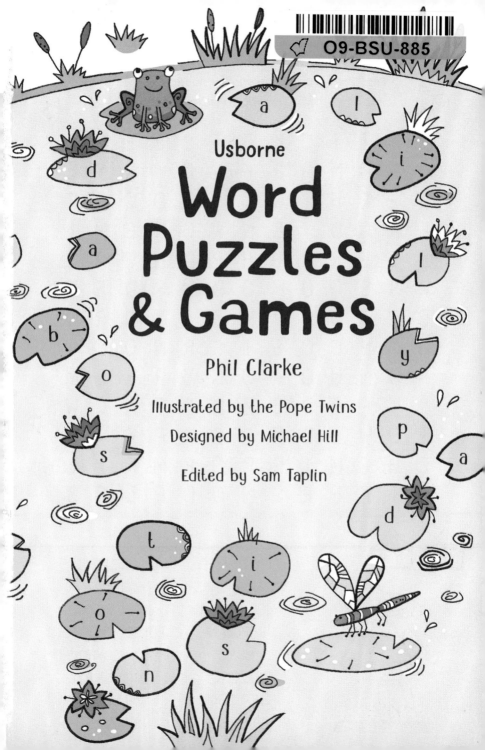

Usborne

Word
Puzzles
& Games

Phil Clarke

Illustrated by the Pope Twins

Designed by Michael Hill

Edited by Sam Taplin

O9-BSU-885

Funfair wordsearch

Find the funfair words below hidden in the grid.
They may be written in any direction.

```
R I T I C K E T S E E N E
O E G N A R E L F I R Y L
L E E H I W O Y A O C E R
L R G D Y B N W C K E M I
E E E R R U H P D H U A C
R S S O O M O D W S D E T
C G J U N P M S I Y Q R O
O O P C O E I C R N O C L
A D N U O R O G Y R R E M
S T E A R C A D E T N C W
T O W E D A E C R A E I K
E H F M I R R O R M A Z E
R I F L E S N O O L L A B
```

FERRIS WHEEL

BUMPER CARS

ICE CREAM

POPCORN

MUSIC

TICKETS

HOT DOG

CAROUSEL

RIDES

ARCADE

RIFLE RANGE

ROLLER COASTER

MERRY-GO-ROUND

MIRROR MAZE

BALLOONS

CROWDS

Which vowel?

Add one of the five vowels a, e, i, o or u to each word below, to make a new word. For example, "shut" could become "shout". Use a different vowel in each word.

1. clam ....

2. wary ....

3. case ....

4. drop ....

5. corn ....

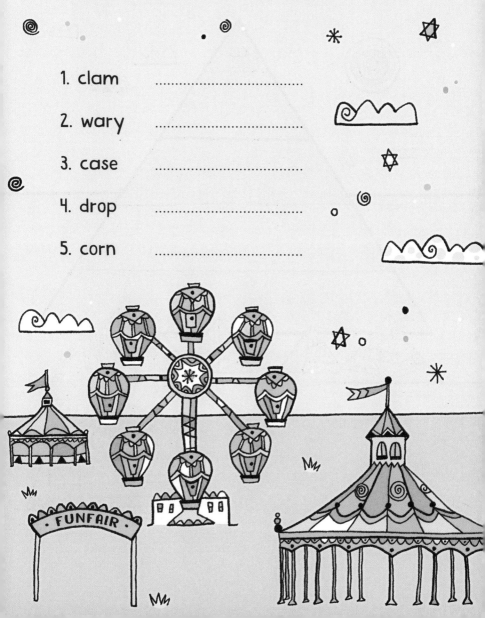

FUNFAIR

Word pyramid

In each section of the pyramid, write a word that can be made by adding one letter into the word above, in any place. Use the clues to help you.

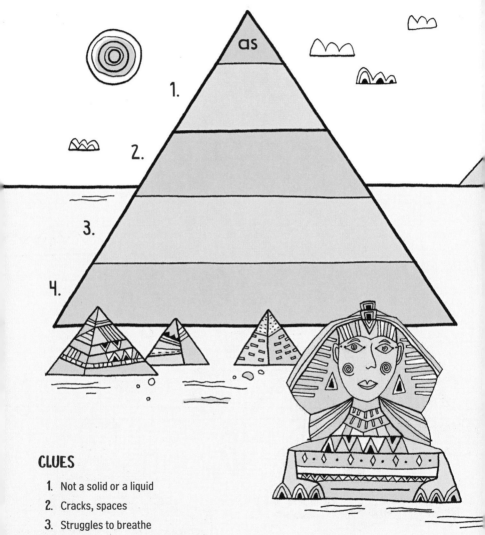

as

1.

2.

3.

4.

CLUES

1. Not a solid or a liquid
2. Cracks, spaces
3. Struggles to breathe
4. Clutches

Pyramid words

The letters of the word "pyramids" are written on the blocks below. Moving from block to block in any direction, how many words of three letters or more can you make from them, without repeating a letter?

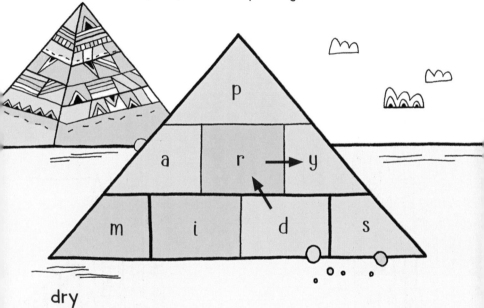

dry

6-10 words - Not bad
11-20 words - Very good
21 words plus - Amazing!

Fit the puzzle blocks into the grid to spell
out the names of six European capitals.

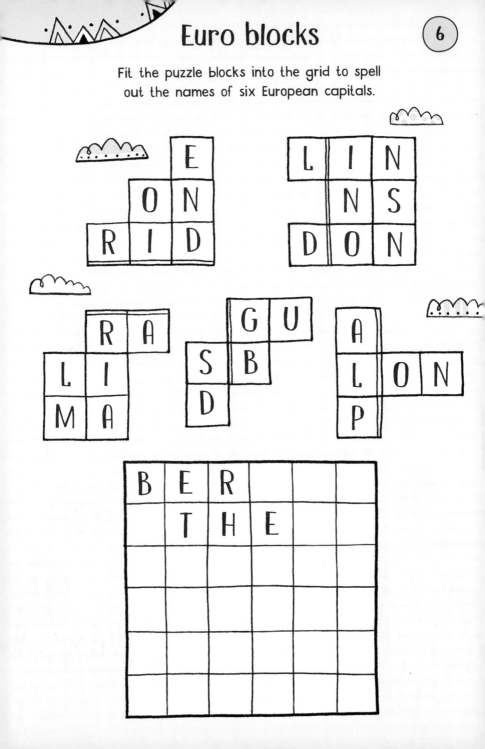

Plant anagrams

Rearrange the letters of these words to make
new words related to plants and trees.

1. asp ....

2. dub ....

3. once ....

4. vein ....

5. hoots ....

6. stun ....

7. flea ....

8. brush ....

9. plate ....

10. talks ....

Hidden words

Underline an insect or creepy-crawly hidden in each sentence below. For example: "It would <u>be eas</u>y to miss."

1. What a pleasant day!
2. She met me briefly to say hello.
3. I'll see you tomorrow or Monday.
4. I was pretty tired afterwards.
5. I let out a gasp — I'd erased all my work!

Planets crisscross

Can you fit the eight planet names into the squares?

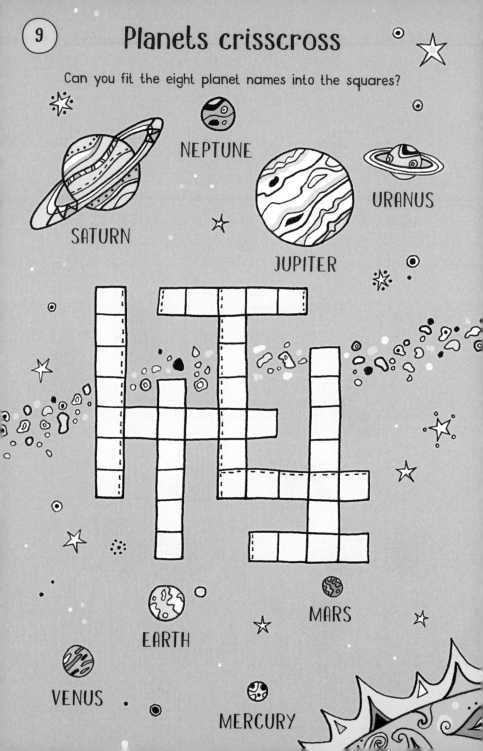

NEPTUNE

SATURN

JUPITER

URANUS

EARTH

MARS

VENUS

MERCURY

Crossword

Solve the clues to fill in the blanks.

ACROSS

1. Star pattern named for a flying horse (7)

6. Opposite of full (5)

7. What you do with food (3)

8. US space agency (4)

10. Thought (4)

12. "I am neither tall ___ short" (3)

13. The path of an object around a star or planet (5)

15. The North Star (7)

DOWN

1. Expecting a child (8)

2. Space, break (3)

3. *Simon ____*, party game (4)

4. How fast something is going (5)

5. The last Space Shuttle to fly, or a legendary sunken island (8)

9. Junk metal (5)

11. Paper-thin metal (4)

14. A length of metal (3)

Baffling books

These books are ordered alphabetically by author's name. Following this order, write the CAPITAL letters from their titles into the spaces below to see an old proverb.

<u>A</u> <u>B</u> _

Walk the plank

A game for two players. You'll
need some paper and a pen.

1

One person is the pirate. That
player thinks of a word, then
draws dashes to show how
many letters it has.

2

The other player says a
letter. If it is in the word,
the pirate fills in the gaps.

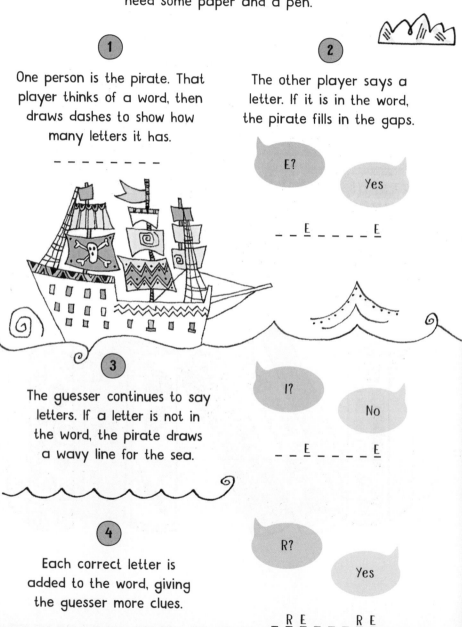

E?

Yes

_ _ E _ _ _ _ E

3

The guesser continues to say
letters. If a letter is not in
the word, the pirate draws
a wavy line for the sea.

I?

No

_ _ E _ _ _ _ E

4

Each correct letter is
added to the word, giving
the guesser more clues.

R?

Yes

_ R E _ _ R E

5

For each wrong letter, the pirate adds further parts to the picture, in this order:

1) Sea

2) Plank

3) Head

4) Body

5) Left leg

6) Right leg

7) Left arm

8) Right arm

9) Start shark fin

10) Finish shark fin

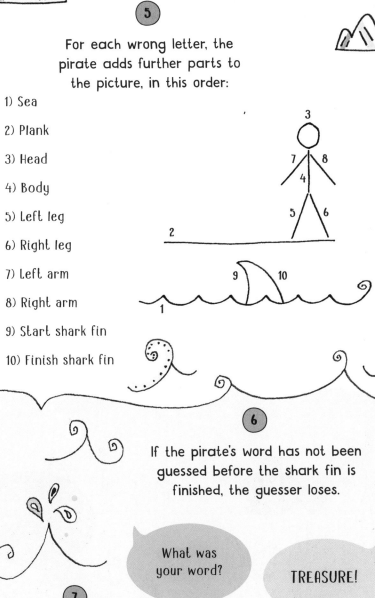

6

If the pirate's word has not been guessed before the shark fin is finished, the guesser loses.

What was your word?

TREASURE!

7

Take turns being the pirate and the guesser.

Word pairs

All but one of these words can be paired up with
another one that has the same meaning.
Circle the word that is on its own.

coast

froth

little

stripe

case

foam

small

big

shell

band

shore

Oceans sudoku

This grid is made up of six blocks, each containing six squares. Fill in the blank squares so that each block, row and column contains all the letters of the word "oceans".

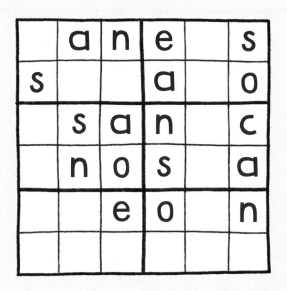

	a	n	e		s
s			a		o
	s	a	n		c
	n	o	s		a
	e	o		n	

Vehicle search

Look at the pictures below, then look for the
names of the vehicles in the grid. They
may be written in any direction.

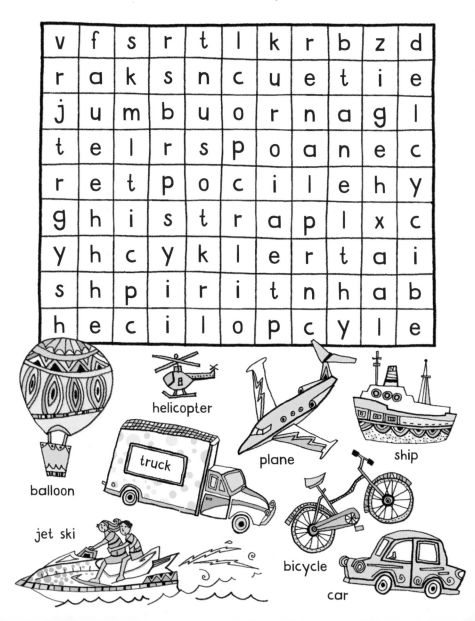

v	f	s	r	t	l	k	r	b	z	d
r	a	k	s	n	c	u	e	t	i	e
j	u	m	b	u	o	r	n	a	g	l
t	e	l	r	s	p	o	a	n	e	c
r	e	t	p	o	c	i	l	e	h	y
g	h	i	s	t	r	a	p	l	x	c
y	h	c	y	k	l	e	r	t	a	i
s	h	p	i	r	i	t	n	h	a	b
h	e	c	i	l	o	p	c	y	l	e

helicopter

plane

ship

balloon

truck

jet ski

bicycle

car

Volcano mix-up

Can you unscramble these groups of letters
to find six words related to volcanoes?

1. has

....

2. mesko

....

3. tracer

....

4. emufs

....

5. puter

....

6. vaal

....

Ghost

A spelling game for
two or more players

1

Someone starts by saying a
letter. The others take turns
in order, adding letters to
continue making a word.

> d

> d-o

> d-o-z

> d-o-z-e

2

Everyone has three lives.
If anyone finishes a word of
four letters or more, they lose
a life and the round ends.

If you lose all three lives, you
become a "ghost" and you're out.

> You lose
> a life!

> Doh! I was thinking
> of "dozen".

3

If you think another player is
making an impossible word,
or is misspelling a word,
you can challenge them.

> f

> f-i

> f-i-g

> f-i-g-a

4

If they can't say what word
they're trying to make, they lose
a life and you start a new round.

> Challenge!

> Ah, you
> got me!

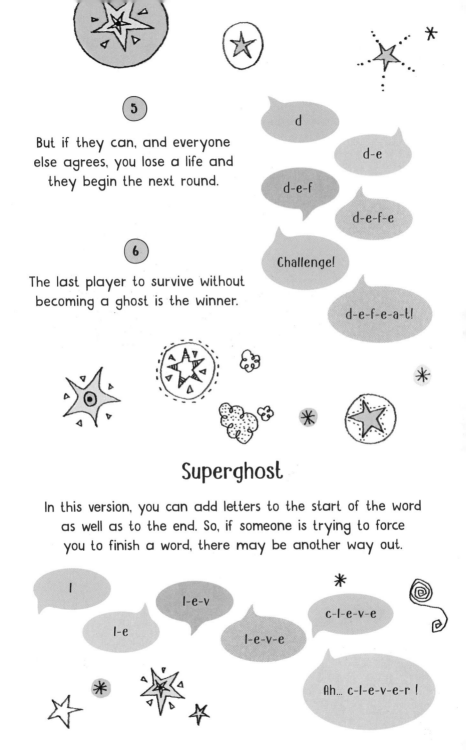

5

But if they can, and everyone else agrees, you lose a life and they begin the next round.

6

The last player to survive without becoming a ghost is the winner.

Superghost

In this version, you can add letters to the start of the word as well as to the end. So, if someone is trying to force you to finish a word, there may be another way out.

Pirate puzzle

Draw a circle around the words that can't
be made from the letters in the word
"pirate", using each letter only once.

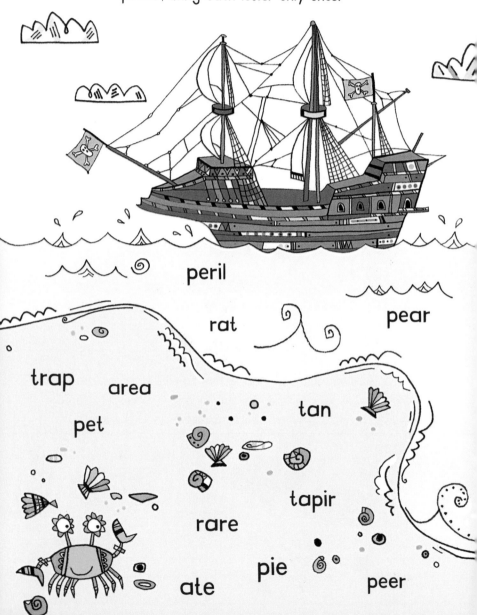

peril

rat

pear

trap

area

pet

tan

tapir

rare

pie

ate

peer

Word target

Write letters in the blank spaces of this target to finish the words. Use the clues at the bottom to find the right answers. Write from the outside of the circle to the middle, so that each word ends with the letter "t."

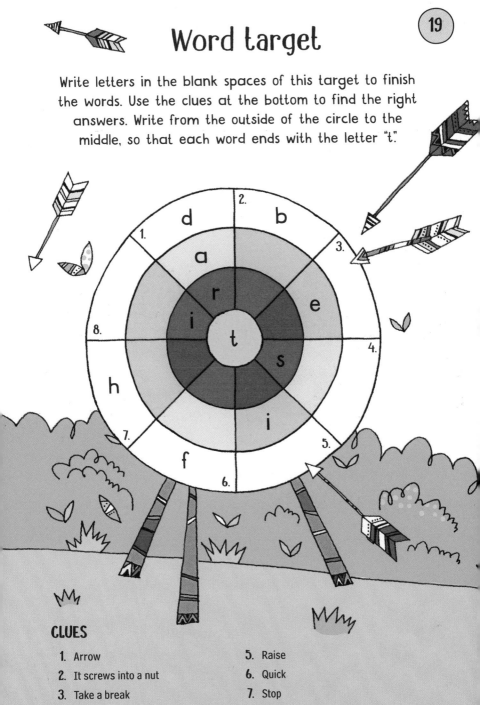

CLUES

1. Arrow
2. It screws into a nut
3. Take a break
4. Finest
5. Raise
6. Quick
7. Stop
8. Thin opening

Rigmarole

A game for three or more players

1 The first player invents a phrase using the "o" that begins the word "one."

One orange octopus

2 The next player repeats the first phrase, then adds another using "two" and "t."

One orange octopus and two terrible toasters

3

The next player uses the "th" sound that begins "three."

One orange octopus, two terrible toasters and three thirsty thieves

4

Continue taking turns like this for as long as you can. If anyone forgets a phrase, or can't think of a new one, the game is over.

One orange octopus, two terrible toasters, three thirsty thieves, four fabulous fairies, five funny fish, six sizzling sausages, seven silk scarves, eight empty envelopes, nine naughty newts and ten terrific trumpets!

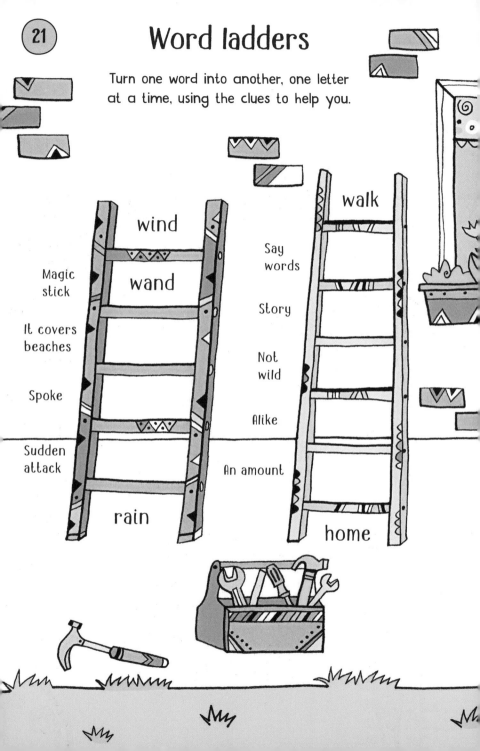

Word ladders

Turn one word into another, one letter at a time, using the clues to help you.

wind

wand

Magic stick

It covers beaches

Spoke

Sudden attack

rain

walk

Say words

Story

Not wild

Alike

An amount

home

old

Opposite of even

Opposite of subtract

Help

Top, cover

Guided

Allow

Used in tennis

new

Winter sudoku

This grid is made up of six blocks, each containing six squares. Fill in the blank squares, so that each block, row and column contains all the letters of the word "winter."

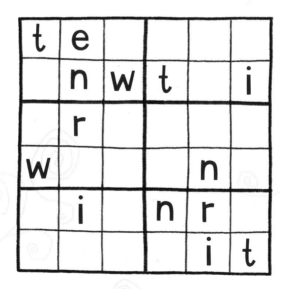

t	e				
	n	w	t		i
	r				
w				n	
	i		n	r	
				i	t

Misfits

Underline the word in each list that
is different from all the others.

1
safe
shielded
protected
vulnerable
guarded

2
cold
arctic
frosty
balmy
chilly

3
door
house
dwelling
abode
home

4
soft
squishy
yielding
pliable
firm

5
rest
strive
unwind
relax
laze

6
banquet
barbecue
council
dinner
feast

Word web

Guide the fly out of the spider's web, avoiding
sticky yellow threads and dead ends. It can't
go along a thread twice. Write the letters
it passes into the spaces to discover
the world's largest spider.

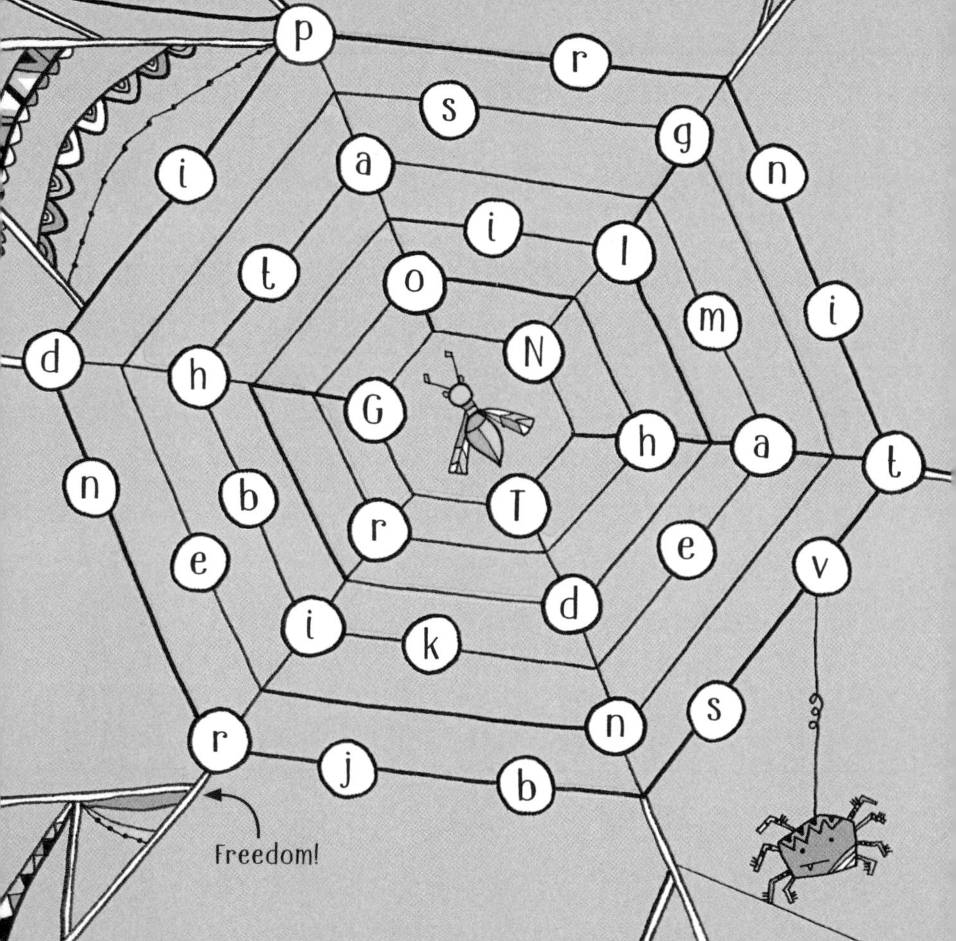

Freedom!

_ _ _ _ _ _ _ -

_ _ _ _ _ _ _ _ _ _

Scrambled bugs

Rearrange the mixed-up words to find
nine bugs, insects or creepy-crawlies.

1. glus ....

2. alef ....

3. nails ....

4. bleeet ....

5. prides ....

6. ticcker ....

7. wargie ....

8. emitter ....

9. brytflute ....

Bird blocks

Fit the puzzle blocks into the grid
to spell out the names of six birds.

Code breaker

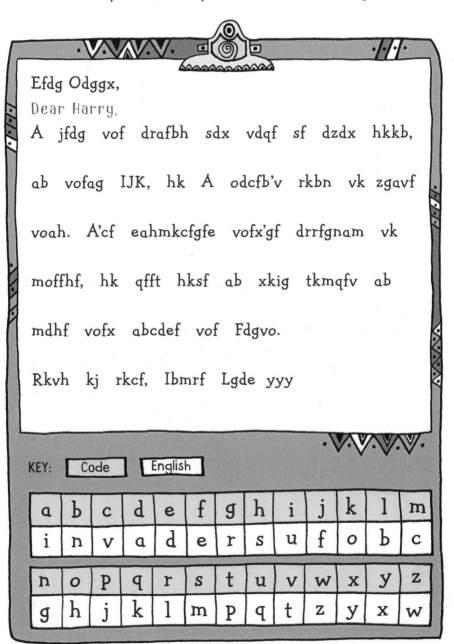

Use the key to help Harry decode his uncle's strange letter.

Efdg Odggx,
Dear Harry,

A jfdg vof drafbh sdx vdqf sf dzdx hkkb,

ab vofag IJK, hk A odcfb'v rkbn vk zgavf

voah. A'cf eahmkcfgfe vofx'gf drrfgnam vk

moffhf, hk qfft hksf ab xkig tkmqfv ab

mdhf vofx abcdef vof Fdgvo.

Rkvh kj rkcf, Ibmrf Lgde yyy

KEY: [Code] [English]

a	b	c	d	e	f	g	h	i	j	k	l	m
i	n	v	a	d	e	r	s	u	f	o	b	c

n	o	p	q	r	s	t	u	v	w	x	y	z
g	h	j	k	l	m	p	q	t	z	y	x	w

Where on Earth?

Use the grid references below to discover
a place explored by a famous scientist.

	A	B	C	D	E
1	R	L	I	N	B
2	O	T	A	W	G
3	E	D	V	U	S
4	A	H	G	F	Z
5	L	S	C	P	A

C4	E5	B1	C2	D5	A4	E2	A2	E3

C1	E3	A5	C2	D1	B3	B5

South American scramble

Can you unscramble these groups of letters
to find six South American animals?

1. holst

....

2. acount

....

3. arajug

....

4. malal

....

5. crodon

....

6. unaagi

....

Last letter

A game for two or more players

1

Choose a theme. Let's say it's "animals". Someone starts by calling out an animal:

giraffe

2

The next person has to think of an animal starting with the last letter of the animal before.

giraff**e**...
elephant

elephant

tiger

rhino

3

Everyone takes turns calling out new animals, without repeating any.

4

The game continues until someone can't think of an animal that follows on from the last one.

Think of ten

A game for three or more players

1

Someone thinks of a theme. For example:

food   animals   countries   vehicles

2

The others have one minute to think of ten things in that category. If they think of ten, they get one point.

> Lion... bear... gazelle... alligator... kangaroo...

3

You all take turns choosing themes. The first to reach five points is the winner.

TIP: If a minute is too easy for you, try 30 seconds.

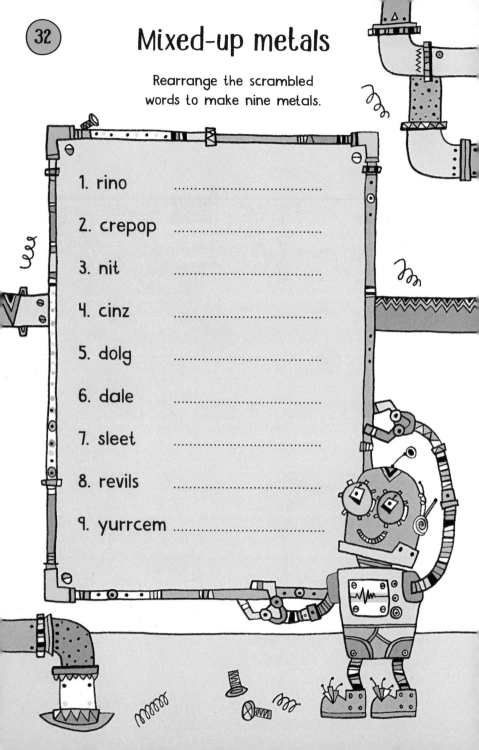

Mixed-up metals

Rearrange the scrambled
words to make nine metals.

1. rino   ....

2. crepop   ....

3. nit   ....

4. cinz   ....

5. dolg   ....

6. dale   ....

7. sleet   ....

8. revils   ....

9. yurrcem   ....

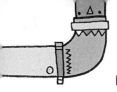

Riddle

Each verse of this riddle gives you a clue
to a letter that makes up its answer, or
to the whole thing. Can you solve it?

My first is in sing,
but it isn't in sink.

My next is in startle,
and also in blink.

My third is in moon,
but it isn't in sun.

My fourth is in seven,
but never in none.

My last is in queen,
but it isn't in king.

My whole has five fingers,
yet can't feel a thing.

~~sing~~
~~sink~~

Answer: g _ _ _ _

Rainbow crisscross

Can you fit all seven words into the squares?

green

blue

indigo

yellow

violet

orange

red

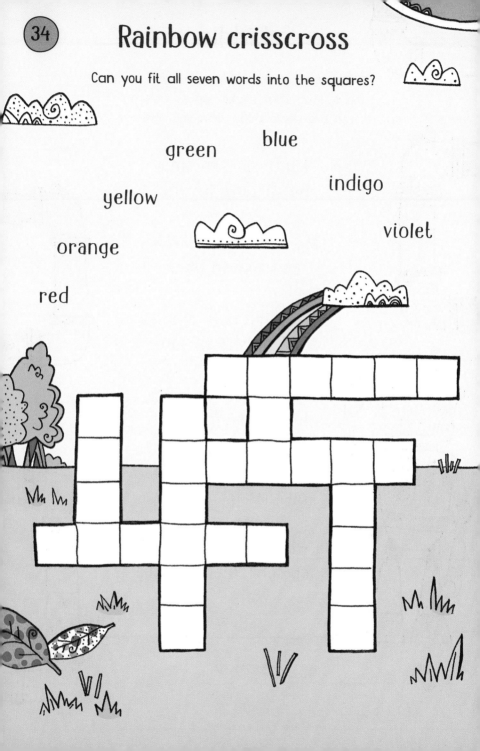

Squirrel sudoku

This grid is made up of six blocks, each containing six squares. Fill in the blank squares so that each block, row and column contains all the letters of the word ACORNS.

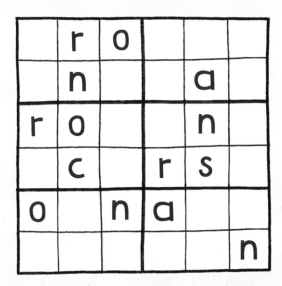

Telephone

A game of garbled messages
for five or more players

1

Everyone stands in a long line or
a big circle. One person thinks of
a message and whispers it very
quietly to the person on their left.

I don't like cabbage,
but I really hate
mushrooms...

2

The second player quickly
whispers the message
to the next player.

I've got my sandwich,
but I really ate
mushroom...

3

The message is passed all
the way to the last player.

I've got my salmon
and a really great
marshmallow...

The gold mice sat
on a really great
Martian...

4

When it reaches the last player,
the first player announces the
original message, then the
last player tells everyone
what it has become...

The goldmine sat
on a silly green
Martian!

Food and drink

Underline a food and a drink hidden in each sentence below. For example: "Each <u>team</u> take a <u>map, please</u>."

1. Hey, Nicola! What a cool party!

2. So, Dave is quite nice, really?

3. Rebecca kept talking on the topic of feeding birds.

4. Poppy, give it back to Tom at once.

5. Tulsa, USA, gets lots of storms – I saw a terrific one.

Word finder

How many words of three letters or more can you make from the nine letters below, using only letters that touch each other, and each just once? Can you find a nine-letter word for something tasty?

cat

6-10 words - Not bad
11-20 words - Very good
21 words plus - Amazing!

The emperor's cat

A game for three or more players

1

The first player starts off by describing the emperor's cat with a word beginning with "A".

The emperor's cat is an *adorable* cat.

2

The others take turns to do the same, each using a different word beginning with "A".

The emperor's cat is an *athletic* cat.

The emperor's cat is an *awful* cat.

3

The first player then starts a round of "B" words, and the others do the same, and so on.

The emperor's cat is a *Burmese* cat.

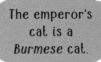

The emperor's cat is a *brilliant* cat.

4

The emperor's cat is a *blue* cat.

When you reach "X" you can use words that start "ex-". Can you make it all the way to "Z"?

The emperor's cat is an *exciting* cat!

Alphabet pets

Once you've all become experts at the emperor's cat, you can try this version, where you also get to think up alphabet-themed jobs, pets and names. (Skip X, if you like.)

The acrobat's ant is an arrogant ant, and her name is Annabelle.

The mayor's moose is a merry moose, and his name is Maurice.

The zookeeper's zebra is a zany zebra, and his name is Zac.

Whodunnit?

Use the missing letters from this crime report
to help Inspector Smart discover the culprit.

The thef_ of t_e Sultan's prize ruby was discov_red a_ midnig_t last n_ght by s_curity guard Mr. John Shah. The _abulous gem was lent to the Hardy Museum only on Fr_day. It_ manager, Mrs. Ann Hardy, has _ade it c_ystal clear that it wa_ checked at eig_t o'clock by jewel expert Mr. H_rry Sharp. The cleane_, Mrs. Olive Hart, said that she had seen a suspicious-looking man in the museum the nigh_ before.

Answer:

Solve the clues to work out which number stands for which letter, and discover some well-balanced birds.

A 1832 is a young horse.

The 4886 orbits the Earth.

A 96352 is a slow garden creature.

You wave a 1237 to support your country.

Answer:

___ ___ ___ ___ ___ ___ ___ ___ ___
1   2   3   4   5   6   7   8   9

Cross-fit

Try to fit all six words into the white squares of each grid, writing across and down.

1.

p

aloud
photo
ridge
swamp
super
phone

ankle
shell
socks
easel
share
cakes

2.

s

3.

o

mayor
rainy
birds
spear
olive
bloom

For each word below, make a new word
by moving one letter to another place.
For example, "leap" becomes "plea".

1. now ....

2. thin ....

3. horse ....

4. earth ....

5. later ....

6. cloud ....

7. south ....

8. height ....

9. pits ....

10. glare ....

Cheese search

Find these 12 cheeses hidden in the grid.
They may be written in any direction.

E	C	T	R	E	B	M	E	M	A	C
L	H	A	G	H	I	A	B	O	R	A
A	E	Q	E	N	T	D	N	Z	O	L
D	D	A	N	E	F	E	T	Z	H	P
Y	D	U	F	E	M	O	I	A	A	M
E	A	L	O	Z	N	O	G	R	O	G
L	R	M	C	G	E	H	M	E	B	P
S	T	I	L	T	Q	E	K	L	W	H
N	D	A	N	I	S	H	B	L	U	E
E	M	A	D	A	C	Y	Y	A	S	T
W	H	Z	N	O	T	L	I	T	S	E

BRIE	DANISH BLUE	EDAM
CHEDDAR	CAMEMBERT	GOUDA
PARMESAN	STILTON	MOZZARELLA
WENSLEYDALE	FETA	GORGONZOLA

Jigwords

Four words have been broken up into three jigsaw
pieces each. Link the pieces and write the words below.

lop

sly

cur

tic

lyf

tas

fan

gal

ing

jel

ish

iou

_ _ _ _ _ _ _ _ _   _ _ _ _ _ _ _ _ _

_ _ _ _ _ _ _ _ _   _ _ _ _ _ _ _ _ _

Comparisons

Mark the correct answer for each comparison. For example, "Grass is to ground as hair is to head" means that grass grows on the ground like hair grows on a head.

Example   Grass is to ground as hair is to:

cut   rabbit   (head)

1. Brain is to skull as heart is to:

ribcage   love   spade

2. Horse is to foal as bear is to:

hay   carry   cub

3. Swim is to water as fly is to:

land   spider   air

4. Help is to hinder as mend is to:

break   improve   fix

5. Oregano is to herb as ginger is to:

spice   bread   hair

Guess the letter

A game for two or more players

A B C D E F G H I J K L M N O P Q R S T U V W X Y Z

1

One person thinks of a letter.
Example: K

2

The rest take turns to ask questions that can be answered Yes or No to try and find the letter.

Does it come before N?

Yes

3

The questioners get a total of ten questions between them. Guesses count as questions.

Is it a vowel?

No

Is it in the word "cabbage"?

No

Is it in the word "hijack"?

Yes

Is it J?

No

4

If someone guesses right, they win, if no one guesses, the thinker wins.

Is it K?

Yes!

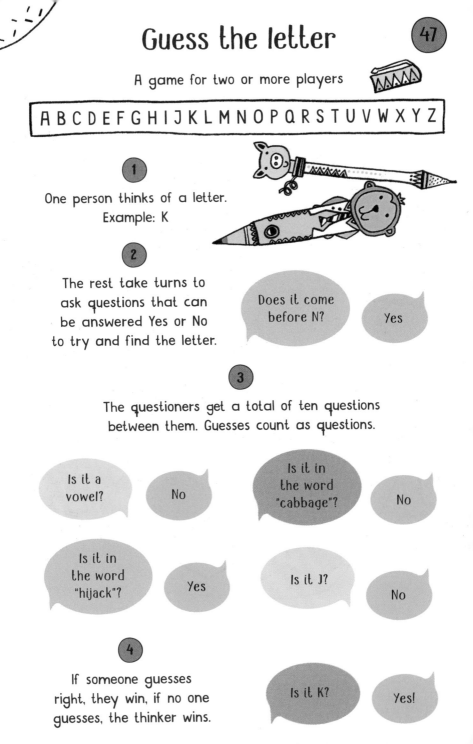

Honeycomb

Fit the words below into the honeycomb,
circling clockwise around the brown cells.
Each word starts in an orange cell.

secret   ~~nectar~~   beauty   carpet

bright   saucer   cherry

Synonyms

Synonyms are words that have the same meaning, like
gift and present. Look at the words below, then mark
them ✓ if they are synonyms or ✗ if they are not.

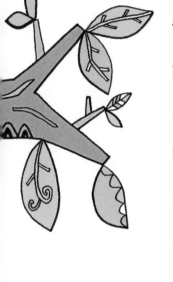

1. small   little

2. sit   stand

3. start   begin

4. same   alike

5. wintry   warm

6. shout   yell

7. brave   strong

8. timid   shy

9. sudden   slow

10. simple   easy

Quizzle

A guessing game for four or more players

1

One or more people leave the room.
The others choose a verb (a doing
word) such as "read" or "jump".

Let's choose
"swim"

Okay!

2

The guessers are called back in, and
question the others about the word.
Everyone uses "quizzle" in its place.

Do you quizzle
in the house?

Are you good
at quizzling?

No, I don't
quizzle at home.

Not bad, but Rosie
quizzles better!

3

The game continues until the secret
word is guessed. Take turns to be
the guessers and the quizzlers.

Do you need any
special gear to
quizzle?

I did when I
started quizzling,
but not anymore.

Word match

For each group of words, see if you can draw around the one that means the same as the word on the label.

Madame

bestow   except

accept   acquit

exact   accent

receive

laze   loose

lose   loss

less   lost

misplace

aloud

along

aloof

allowed

alloyed

avowed

permitted

muddle   medal

meddle   model

metal   middle

interfere

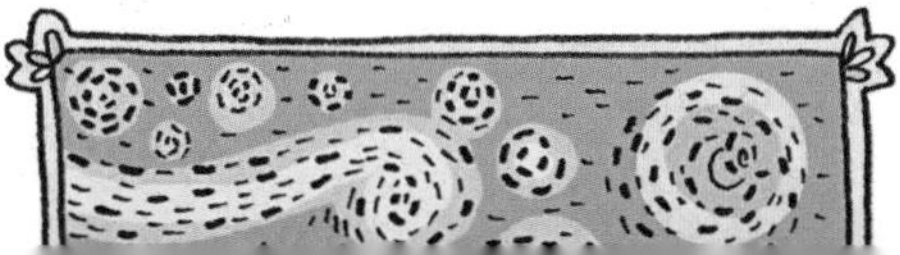

Crossword

Solve the clues to fill in the blanks.

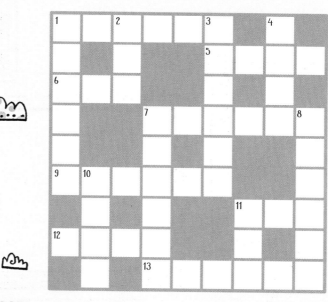

ACROSS

1. Large ship that carries oil (6)
5. Individual part (4)
6. Perform in a play or movie (3)
7. Woodland animal with a black-and-white face (6)
9. Member of a ship's crew (6)
11. Enemy (3)
12. Foamy trail behind a boat (4)
13. Ship's chimney (6)

DOWN

1. Gratitude (6)
2. It's used to catch lots of fish (3)
3. Hinged flap at the rear of a boat, used to steer it (6)
4. The regular coming in and going out of the sea (4)
7. Faith (6)
8. Uncover, show (6)
10. Opposite of towards (4)
11. Amusement (3)

Word chains

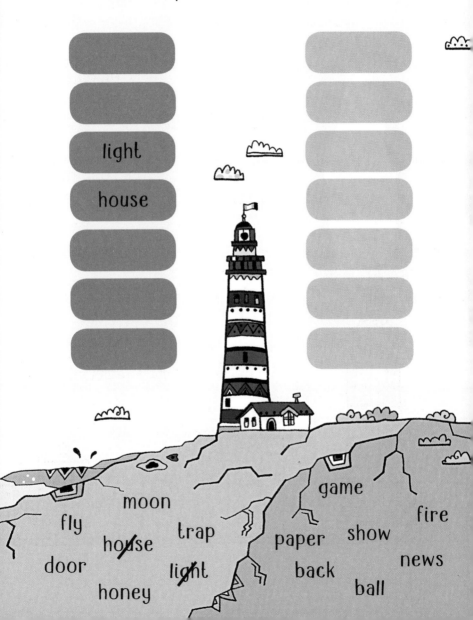

New York skyline

Write these New York City places downwards in the blocks in alphabetical order. Then copy out the letters from the yellow blocks (reading down and along) into the spaces at the bottom to see the name of a famous New York poet.

WEST SIDE

~~BRONX~~

HARLEM

THE MET

ROCKEFELLER CENTER

GRAND CENTRAL

CENTRAL PARK

RIVERDALE

EAST SIDE

MADISON AVENUE

ONE WORLD TRADE CENTER

TIMES SQUARE

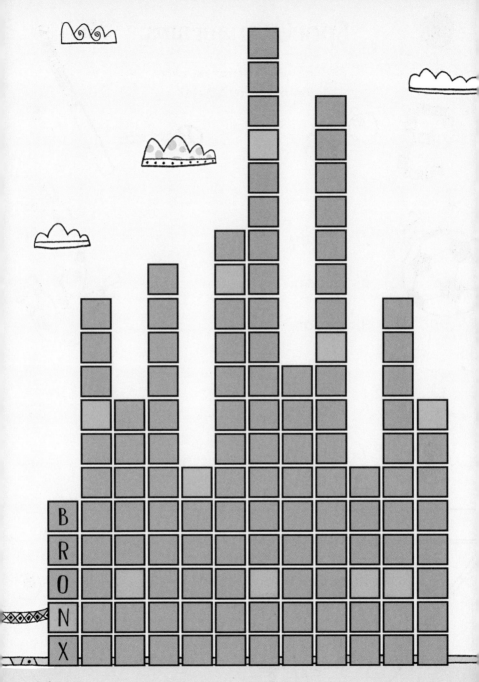

BRONX

N

Sports anagrams

Can you unscramble all
the mixed-up sports?

1. flog ....

2. chokey ....

3. caring ....

4. gybur ....

5. lobaloft ....

6. babellas ....

7. takings ....

8. kebabstall ....

9. blowing ....

10. netsin ....

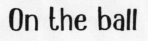

On the ball

Draw around the sports hidden
among the letters. Can you find 20?

shoockery
tencaratsquashes
baseballcycadslimming
amusesomecherryrunning
batfootballrugsnookerange
faintingskiingthinkaratenses
ratenniseyeballhockeytricked
buckswimmingrownetballaugh
snowballarcheryoddballcycling
rugbyfurballcricketraidingpin
whispookierfencingmothball
ruiningsumotherdivingoal
scarequashdiscussels
stridingbatopsy
gulfroger

Eat the alphabet

A game for two or more players

1

Agree which letters are too hard (such as Q, X and Z) and leave them out.

2

Someone says that they're going to eat a food that starts with an A:

> I'm HUNGRY!
> I'm going to eat an apricot.

3

The next player then thinks of a food beginning with B:

> I'm HUNGRY!
> I'm going to eat some bread.

4

The game continues with
everyone taking turns as you
work through the alphabet:

I'm HUNGRY!
I'm going to eat
some cherries.

I'm HUNGRY!
I'm going to eat
some dates.

I'm HUNGRY!
I'm going to
eat an éclair.

5

The game carries on until someone
can't think of a food beginning with
the next letter. Can you eat all the
way through the alphabet?

Vanished vowels

Can you fill in the missing
vowels from the letter below?

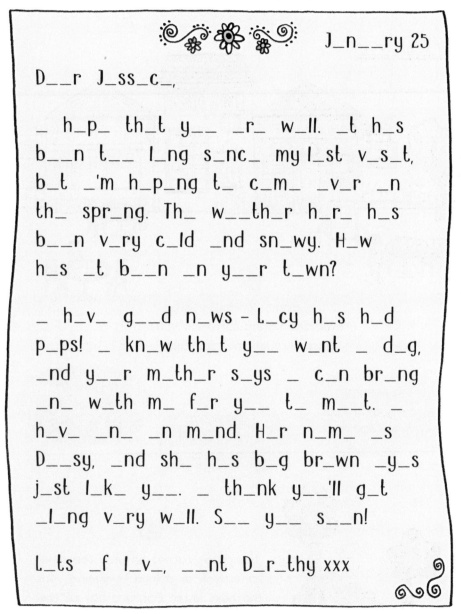

J_n__ry 25

D__r J_ss_c_,

_ h_p_ th_t y__ _r_ w_ll. _t h_s
b__n t__ l_ng s_nc_ my l_st v_s_t,
b_t _'m h_p_ng t_ c_m_ _v_r _n
th_ spr_ng. Th_ w__th_r h_r_ h_s
b__n v_ry c_ld _nd sn_wy. H_w
h_s _t b__n _n y__r t_wn?

_ h_v_ g__d n_ws - L_cy h_s h_d
p_ps! _ kn_w th_t y__ w_nt _ d_g,
_nd y__r m_th_r s_ys _ c_n br_ng
_n_ w_th m_ f_r y__ t_ m__t. _
h_v_ _n_ _n m_nd. H_r n_m_ _s
D__sy, _nd sh_ h_s b_g br_wn _y_s
j_st l_k_ y__. _ th_nk y__'ll g_t
_l_ng v_ry w_ll. S__ y__ s__n!

L_ts _f l_v_, __nt D_r_thy xxx

Spring sudoku

This grid is made up of six blocks, each containing six squares. Fill in the blank squares, so that each block, row and column contains all the letters of the word "spring."

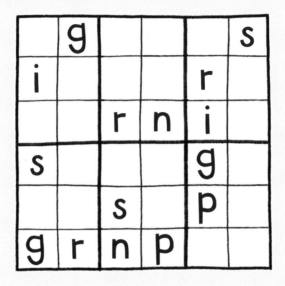

Spiral galaxies

The space words below have been
curled into tight spirals and hidden
in the grid. An example is given.
Can you find them all?

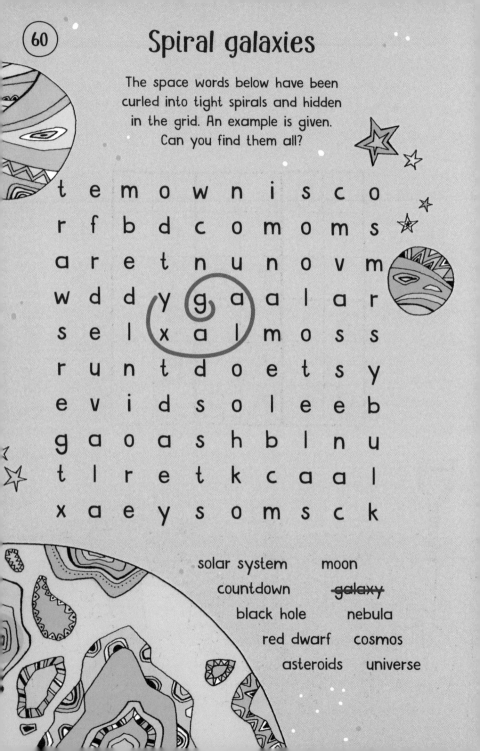

```
t  e  m  o  w  n  i  s  c  o
r  f  b  d  c  o  m  o  m  s
a  r  e  t  n  u  n  o  v  m
w  d  d  y  g  a  a  l  a  r
s  e  l  x  a  l  m  o  s  s
r  u  n  t  d  o  e  t  s  y
e  v  i  d  s  o  l  e  e  b
g  a  o  a  s  h  b  l  n  u
t  l  r  e  t  k  c  a  a  l
x  a  e  y  s  o  m  s  c  k
```

solar system   moon

countdown   ~~galaxy~~

black hole   nebula

red dwarf   cosmos

asteroids   universe

Verb power

Zac's spaceship is powered by verbs (doing words).
Can you find ten to help him reach his destination?

Zac

zone

flea

swim

jump

sore

mauve

glade

hurtle

wig

depart

lamp

new

zoom

damp

soar

piece

spin

move

turtle

brisk

flee

glide

Paint mixing

The names of the artist's paints have been
split in two — draw lines to pair them up.

let

nder   yel   saf

viol   ora

nge   crim

mar   low

son   fron

scar   pur   oon

ple   lave   et

Find the city

Read the clues and fill in the two missing letters.
Then join up the new letters to make the
name of a famous capital city.

1. It tastes salty   sea __ __ ter

2. Daylight   sun __ __ ine

3. Common   ord __ __ ary

4. Sound of a phone   rin __ __ one

5. Citrus drink   lem __ __ ade

6. House for a flying pet   bir __ __ age

Answer: ....

Crambo

A game for three or more players

1

One player thinks of a word, then announces another word that rhymes with it:

> I know a word that rhymes with "bee".

2

The rest then make their guesses, but without saying the rhyming word:

> Is it very big and wet?

> No, it's not the sea.

3

The first player then confirms or denies the rhyme that was guessed:

> Does it jump and bite?

> No, it's not a flea.

4

The game continues until the word is guessed, or everyone gives up, then someone else thinks of a new rhyme.

> Does it have branches?

> Is it a drink?

> Yes! It is a tree.

> No, it isn't tea.

Riddle

Each verse of this riddle gives you a clue
to a letter that makes up its answer, or
to the whole thing. Can you solve it?

My first is in flies,
but it isn't in fleas.

My next is in beans,
but it isn't in bees.

My third is in feelers,
and also in wings.

My fourth is in ripens,
but never in spring.

My fifth is in fleece,
but it isn't in flame.

My last is in beetle,
but never in blame.

My legs are as many as
the letters in my name.

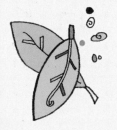

flies
fleas

Answer: i _ _ _ _ _ _

Pigpen cipher

Pigpen is a secret cipher you can use to write messages to your friends. See if you can use the key at the bottom to translate the ones below.

1.

2.

KEY

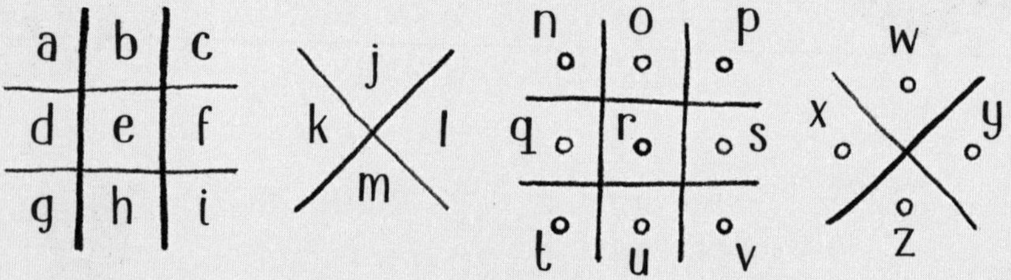

a	b	c
d	e	f
g	h	i

j k l m

n	o	p
q	r	s
t	u	v

w x y z

Broken words

Draw lines to match up the three-letter
words to make ten six-letter words.

ray

hem

the

red

see

kin

act

ant

imp

bet

cot

one

pet

nap

ton

win

led

try

pup

how

Tongue twisters

These crazy phrases are incredibly tricky to say. How fast can you say them before you stumble?

Fred fed Ted bread; Ted fed Fred bread.

The big black bug bit the big black bear, but the big black bear bit the big black bug back!

Toy boat... toy boat... toy boat... toy boat...

Spell it backwards

A game for two or more players

(1)

In this game, one person thinks of a word, then slowly starts to spell it out backwards.

G...N...I...

(2)

People can guess whenever they like. If they're wrong, either carry on from where you left off, or start again if you prefer.

Thing?

No. P... M...

Jumping?

No. A...

(3)

The first person to guess the word wins, and they start a new game.

Camping!

Puzzling proverbs

70

Below are some old sayings whose beginnings
and endings have become mixed up. Can you
draw lines to match them up correctly?

1. You can take a horse to water, but... ...don't fix it.

2. People who live in glass houses... ...don't make a right.

3. Too many cooks... ...is the best policy.

4. If it ain't broke... ...do as the Romans do.

5. Two wrongs... ...are better than one.

6. The early bird... ...you can't make it drink.

7. Birds of a feather... ...should not throw stones.

8. A watched pot... ...catches the worm.

9. When in Rome... ...flock together.

10. Two heads... ...spoil the broth.

11. Honesty... ...never boils.

Forbidden

A game for three or more players

1

In this game, you must answer questions without saying Yes or No, or using a forbidden letter.

2

One person is the questioner. This player chooses the forbidden letter. Don't pick a vowel (a, e, i, o, u) as that would be too hard.

The forbidden letter is "p"

3

The questioner then asks the others questions one at a time. They must answer without breaking the rules.

What do you call a young dog?

I call ours Buster!

4

The questioner keeps going until someone says Yes, No, or the forbidden letter. The last player in wins, and becomes the next questioner.

Do you like playing word games?

What goes with salt?

I enjoy them very much.

Pepper... No - chips! Ah... you got me.

Crossword

Solve the clues to fill in the blanks.

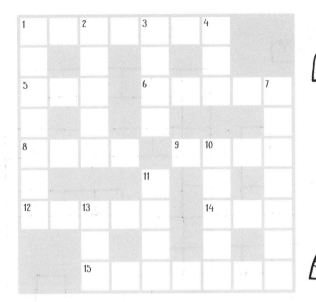

ACROSS

1. Curly-coated dogs (7)
5. December 24 is Christmas ___ (3)
6. Breed of small dog kept by Queen Elizabeth II (5)
8. A Great ____ is a very tall dog (4)
9. Piece of footwear (4)
12. Wild Australian dog (5)
14. Function (3)
15. Small, strong, British dog breed with a flat, wrinkled face (7)

DOWN

1. Begged (7)
2. The Pacific, for example (5)
3. Fortune (4)
4. Title for a knight (3)
7. Big frozen chunk floating in the sea (7)
10. Another word for "dog" (5)
11. Long, sad-sounding cry made by dogs and wolves (4)
13. Pen tip (3)

Round Table crisscross

Can you fit the Knights of the
Round Table into the spaces?

LANCELOT   KAY   TRISTRAM
GALAHAD   ECTOR   MORDRED
PELLEAS   GARETH   GAWAIN
LIONEL   LAMORAK   BORS
    PERCIVAL

Knight search

Find all the six-letter words below, then write them in
the rows in alphabetical order. The circled letters will
spell the founder of the Knights of the Round Table.

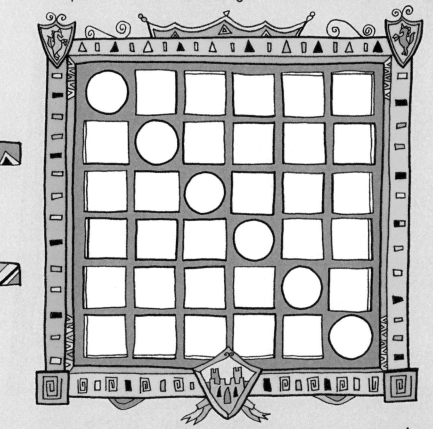

arrows   sword   fights   joust

                   grail

  gallant   brave   loyal   spurs

yonder   steed   battle   mace   rescue

queen   joust   horse   page

       siege

courage   reins   archer   harness

Word ladders

Turn one word into another one letter at a time, using the clues to help you.

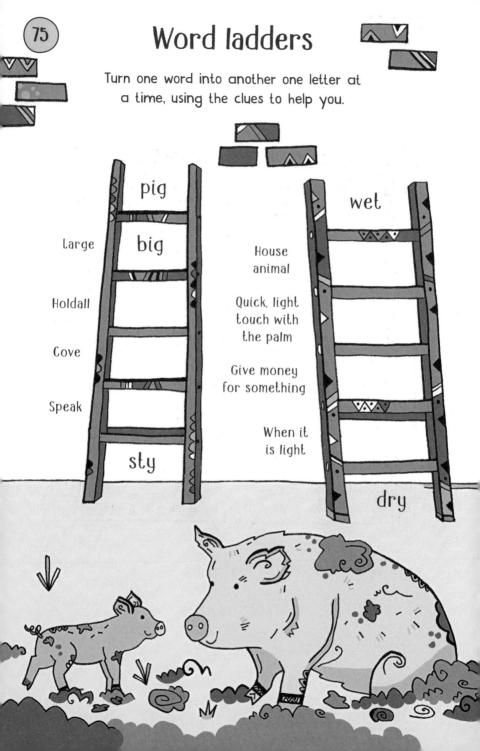

pig

Large — **big**

Holdall

Cove

Speak

sty

wet

House animal

Quick, light touch with the palm

Give money for something

When it is light

dry

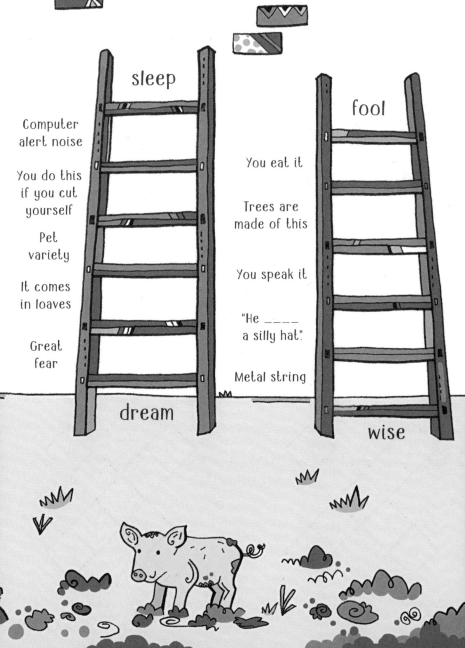

sleep

fool

Computer alert noise

You do this if you cut yourself

Pet variety

It comes in loaves

Great fear

You eat it

Trees are made of this

You speak it

"He _ _ _ _ a silly hat."

Metal string

dream

wise

Word cross

In each word cross, find a letter that completes the three-letter words in the left arms and starts those in the right arms.

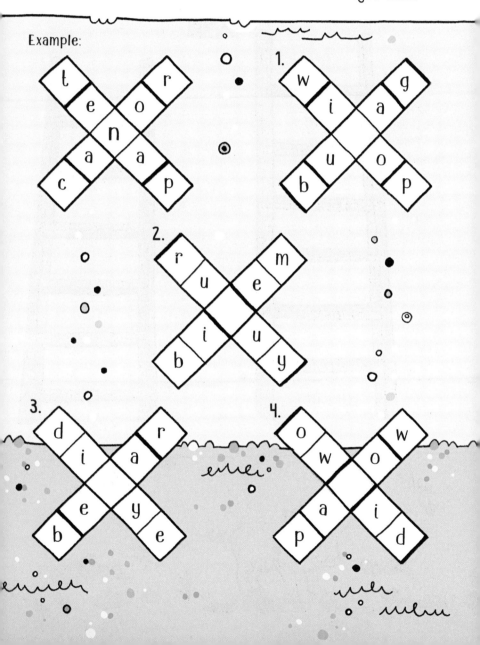

Example:

1.

2.

3.

4.

Who's at home?

Arrange the letters of the alphabet missing
from the tank to discover what lives in it.

Answer: ....

Consequences

A game for two or more players.
You'll need some paper and pens.

1

Make sheets for everyone with eight sections, like this.
An adjective is a describing word, like tall, or kind.

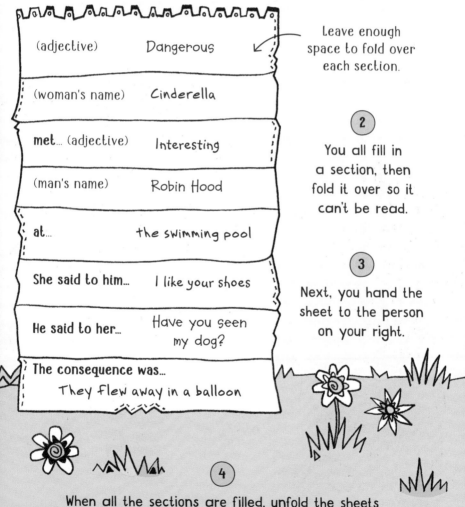

(adjective)	Dangerous
(woman's name)	Cinderella
met... (adjective)	Interesting
(man's name)	Robin Hood
at...	the swimming pool
She said to him...	I like your shoes
He said to her...	Have you seen my dog?
The consequence was...	They flew away in a balloon

Leave enough space to fold over each section.

2

You all fill in a section, then fold it over so it can't be read.

3

Next, you hand the sheet to the person on your right.

4

When all the sections are filled, unfold the sheets
and read out the stories for everyone to hear.

Word maker

A paper-and-pen game you
can play with friends or alone

1

Someone thinks of a word
of five letters or more.

butterfly

2

Now use the letters of
the word to make as
many new words as you
can with at least three
letters, in three minutes.

Use each letter just once
in your words, unless it
appears more than once
in the original word.

For example, "butterfly"
contains these words
and many more:

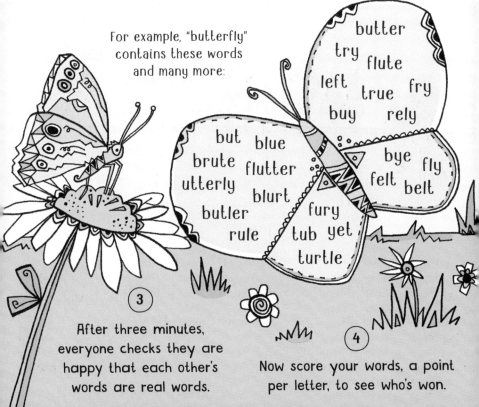

butter
try flute
left true fry
buy rely

but blue
brute flutter
utterly blurt
butler
rule

bye fly
felt belt

fury
tub yet
turtle

3

After three minutes,
everyone checks they are
happy that each other's
words are real words.

4

Now score your words, a point
per letter, to see who's won.

Misfits

Underline the word in each list that
is different from all the others.

1
rare
empty
hollow
vacant
bare

2
hard
tricky
difficult
complex
basic

3
nice
friendly
pleasant
pretty
kind

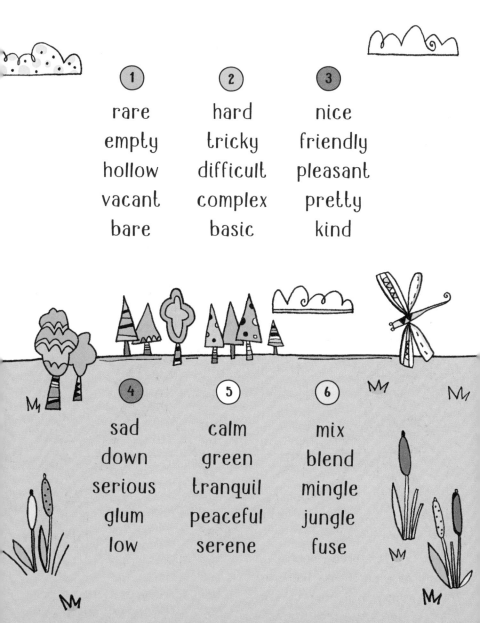

4
sad
down
serious
glum
low

5
calm
green
tranquil
peaceful
serene

6
mix
blend
mingle
jungle
fuse

Solve the clues to work out which number
stands for which letter, and discover
something you might see near a pond.

A 7254 is a hopping creature.

42361 means splendid or impressive.

129 is the opposite of wet.

4831 means happy.

Answer:

___ ___ ___ ___ ___ ___ ___ ___ ___
 1   2   3   4   5   6   7   8   9

Who am I?

A game for two or more players

1

In this game, one person thinks of somebody famous, or someone everyone knows.

2

Everyone else takes turns to ask questions that can be answered Yes or No, to narrow the options.

Are you male?

Yes

Are you old?

Oh yes

3

If Yes or No would be misleading, the thinker can say things like "sometimes" or "I'm not sure".

Do you have a long beard?

Yes

Are you magical?

Can you fly?

Yes

Hmm... sort of

4

If no one can guess, they are given clues until they do, then a new game begins.

Are you Dumbledore?

No

Are you Santa?

Yes!

Rhyme time

Draw around the word that isn't part of a rhyming pair.

twin

rabbit

habit

hearts

bowl

guide

where

tumble

rough

grow

grin

through

meet

shove

mean

drink

eat

sad

though

shoe

slide

hole

curious

queen

mad

stuff

furious

cat

shrink

hare

grumble

tarts

love

Opposites

Circle the word that can't be paired with its opposite.

all loose right rough

push

silent

far cool

sell full huge

light

smooth heavy

empty

warm

buy

near

tiny

none

funny

tight noisy

left

pull

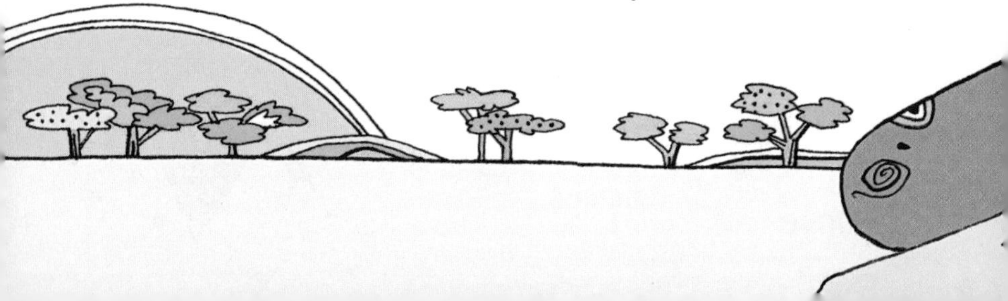

Comparisons

Mark the correct answer for each comparison. For example, "Flock is to sheep as pride is to lions" means that a flock is a group of sheep like a pride is a group of lions.

Example   Flock is to sheep as pride is to:

lions   shame   bees

1. Hammer is to nail as bat is to:

cave   hit   ball

2. Sound is to ear as light is to:

eye   dark   heavy

3. Feathers are to bird as fur is to:

fish   warm   cat

4. Near is to far as tall is to:

distant   height   short

5. Knife is to butcher as fork is to:

spoon   gardener   road

Animal anagrams

See if you can untangle these mixed-up farm animals.

1. gip ....

2. woc ....

3. shoer ....

4. heeps ....

5. toga ....

6. osego ....

7. bartib ....

8. hencick ....

9. yukret ....

Each word starts and ends with the
same letter. Can you fill in the blanks?

1. __ eade __

2. __ ance __

3. __ ivin __

4. __ lassi __

5. __ athtu __

6. __ indo __

7. __ ediu __

8. __ ealt __

9. __ xpos __

10. __ woop __

Penguin puzzle

The penguin chick can only hop onto the pieces of
pack ice with verbs on them. Draw the route
across the safe pieces to its parents.

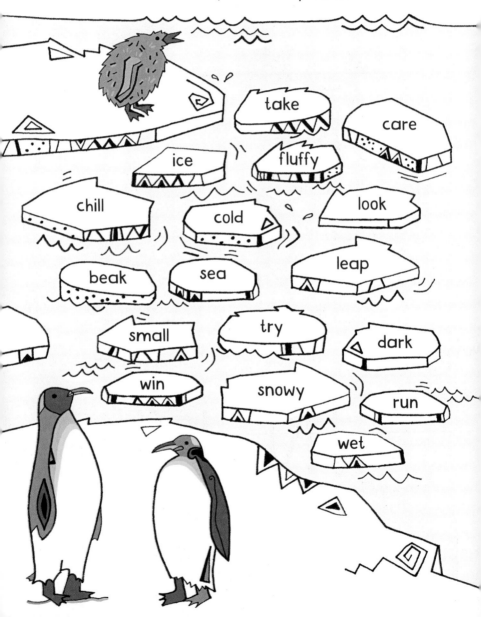

take

care

ice

fluffy

chill

look

cold

beak

sea

leap

small

try

dark

win

snowy

run

wet

Crossword

Solve the clues to fill in the blanks.

ACROSS

1. Turns from liquid to solid at a low temperature (7)
5. Sweet stuff (5)
6. Frozen water (3)
8. You scratch it (4)
10. Lose one's footing on a wet or shiny surface (4)
12. You chew it, but don't swallow it (3)
13. Undersea swimmer (5)
15. Take cover (7)

DOWN

1. Angling (7)
2. A bird lays it (3)
3. None (4)
4. Ability (5)
7. _ _ _ _ _ _ _ penguins are the largest of all penguins (7)
9. Approaches (5)
11. Lazy (4)
14. Animal doctor (3)

20 questions

A game for two or more players

1

One person thinks of something. It can be anything at all, but it must be possible to guess or it's no fun.

2

The rest try to find out what it is by asking the thinker questions that can only be answered Yes or No.

Is it bigger than a toaster?

No

Is it alive?

No

3

The thinker must try to answer Yes or No as helpfully as they can. They may say "Sometimes", "Not sure", or "I can't say" if Yes or No would be misleading.

Can I wear it?

No

Does it need batteries?

Yes

Can it play music?

Yes

Is it a radio?

No

4

You can only ask 20 questions, however many are playing. Guesses count as questions.

Yes!

Is it a phone?

Leaping letters

For each word pair below, make two new words by moving a letter from the first word to the second word.

Example

month .... moth → wings .... wigs

1. broom .... tale

2. knew .... money

3. sight .... ear

4. when .... itch

5. gold .... bean

6. world .... fair

7. reed .... had

8. clever .... sore

9. three .... edge

10. brain .... root

Playing around

See if you can fit all the games
below into the spiral. Each game
starts and ends in a red square.

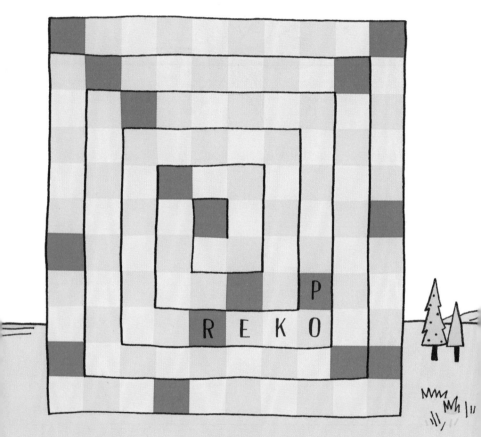

P
R E K O

STILTS   TUG OF WAR   WHIST

POKER   SIMON SAYS   STATUES

RUMMY   DOMINOES   OLD MAID

POOHSTICKS   SEE SAW   SPINNING TOP

SNAKES AND LADDERS   YO YO   ROCK PAPER SCISSORS

Country blocks

Fit the puzzle blocks into the grid to
spell out the names of six countries.

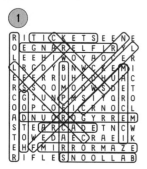

1.

2.
1. claim
2. weary
3. cause
4. droop
5. acorn

3.
1. gas
2. gaps
3. gasps
4. grasps

4.
aid, aids, aim, air, airy, amid, arid, diary, dim, dram, dry, maid, maids, map, mar, Mary, paid, pair, par, prim, primary, pry, raid, raids, ram, rap, rid, rids, rim

6.

B	E	R	L	I	N
A	T	H	E	N	S
L	O	N	D	O	N
P	R	A	G	U	E
L	I	S	B	O	N
M	A	D	R	I	D

7.
1. sap
2. bud
3. cone
4. vine
5. shoot
6. nuts
7. leaf
8. shrub
9. petal
10. stalk

8.
1. What a pleas<u>ant</u> day!
2. She met me brief<u>ly</u> to say hello.
3. I'll see you tomorrow <u>or Monday</u>.
4. <u>I was</u> pretty tired afterwards.
5. I let out a gasp – <u>I'd</u> erased all my work!

9.

10.

P	E	G	A	S	U	S
R		A		A	P	A
E	M	P	T	Y	E	A	T
G			S	E	L
N	A	S	A	I	D	E	A
A	C	F	N
N	O	R	O	R	B	I	T
T	A	I	A	I
P	O	L	A	R	I	S

11.

A BOOK TIGHT SHUT IS BUT A BLOCK OF PAPER

13.
big

14.

o	a	n	e	c	s
s	e	c	a	n	o
e	s	a	n	o	c
c	n	o	s	e	a
a	c	e	o	s	n
n	o	s	c	a	e

15.

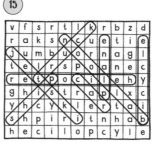

16.
1. ash
2. smoke
3. crater
4. fumes
5. erupt
6. lava

18.
peril area tan rare peer

19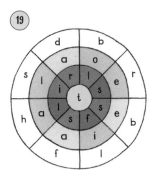

21

wind	walk	old
wand	talk	odd
sand	tale	add
said	tame	aid
raid	same	lid
rain	some	led
	home	let
		net
		new

22

t	e	i	r	w	n
r	n	w	t	e	i
i	r	n	w	t	e
w	t	e	i	n	r
e	i	t	n	r	w
n	w	r	e	i	t

23
1. vulnerable
2. balmy
3. door
4. firm
5. strive
6. council

24
Goliath bird-eating spider

25
1. slug
2. flea
3. snail
4. beetle
5. spider
6. cricket
7. earwig
8. termite
9. butterfly

26

c	a	n	a	r	y
f	a	l	c	o	n
m	a	g	p	i	e
p	u	f	f	i	n
t	h	r	u	s	h
p	i	g	e	o	n

27

Dear Harry,

I fear the aliens may take me away soon, in their UFO, so I haven't long to write this. I've discovered they're allergic to cheese, so keep some in your pocket in case they invade the Earth.

Lots of love, Uncle Brad xxx

28

GALAPAGOS ISLANDS

29
1. sloth
2. toucan
3. jaguar
4. llama
5. condor
6. iguana

32
1. iron
2. copper
3. tin
4. zinc
5. gold
6. lead
7. steel
8. silver
9. mercury

33
The answer is "glove".

34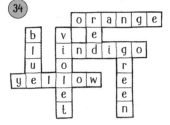

35

a	r	o	n	c	s
s	n	c	o	a	r
r	o	s	c	n	a
n	c	a	r	s	o
o	s	n	a	r	c
c	a	r	s	o	n

37

1. Hey, Nicola! What a cool party!
2. So, Dave is quite nice, really?
3. Rebecca kept talking on the topic of feeding birds.
4. Poppy, give it back to Tom at once.
5. Tulsa, USA, gets lots of storms - I saw a terrific one.

38

ace, act, are, ark, ate, cake, car, care, cat, cater, ear, eat, era, face, facet, fact, fake, faker, far, fare, fat, fate, freak, fret, fruit, **fruitcake**, fur, race, rake, rat, rate, react, rut, take, taker, tar, tea, teak, tear, turf, Turk

40

The thief is Mrs Hart

41

flamingos

42

s	u	p	e	r
w		h		i
a	l	o	u	d
m		t		g
p	h	o	n	e

s	o	c	k	s
h		a		h
a	n	k	l	e
r		e		l
e	a	s	e	l

b	i	r	d	s
l		a		p
o	l	i	v	e
o		n		a
m	a	y	o	r

43

1. own
2. hint
3. shore
4. heart
5. alter
6. could
7. shout
8. eighth
9. spit
10. large

44

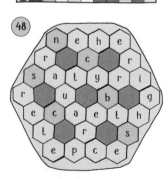

45

curiously fantastic galloping jellyfish

46

1. ribcage 2. cub 3. air 4. break 5. spice

49

1. ✓   6. ✓
2. ✗   7. ✗
3. ✓   8. ✓
4. ✓   9. ✗
5. ✗   10. ✓

48

51

accept   lose
allowed   meddle

52

T	A	N	K	E	R		T	
H		E			U	N	I	T
A	C	T			D		D	
N			B	A	D	G	E	R
K		E		E		E		E
S	A	I	L	O	R			V
	W		I			F	O	E
W	A	K	E			U		A
	Y		F	U	N	N	E	L

53

honey	news
moon	paper
light	back
house	fire
fly	ball
trap	game
door	show

54

```
                O
                N
            E       R
            W       O
            O       C
            R       K
        M   L   E
      G     A   D   F
    C   R   D   T   E   T
    E   A   I   R   L   I
    N   N   S   A   R   M
    T   E   D   O   D   I   E   E   W
    R   A   C   N   E   V   R   S   E
    A   S   E   H   A   C   E   C   T   S   S
  B   L   T   N   A   V   E   R   E   H   Q   T
  R   P   S   T   R   E   N   D   N   E   U   S
  O   A   I   R   L   N   T   A   T   M   A   I
  N   R   D   A   E   U   E   L   L   E   E   R   D
  X   K   E   L   M   E   R   E   R   T   E   E
```

WALT WHITMAN

55

1. golf
2. hockey
3. racing
4. rugby
5. football
6. baseball
7. skating
8. basketball
9. bowling
10. tennis

56

shoockery
tencarat**squash**es
baseballcycads**limming**
amusesomecherry**running**
bat**football**rugs**snooker**ange
fainting**skiing**think**karate**nses
ra**tennis**eyeball**hockey**tricked
buck**swimming**rown**netball**augh
snowball**archery**oddball**cycling**
rugbyfurball**cricket**raidingpin
whispookier**fencing**mothball
ruining**sumo**ther**diving**oal
scarequash**discus**sels
st**riding**batopsy
gulfroger

58

January 25

Dear Jessica,

I hope that you are well. It has been too long since my last visit, but I'm hoping to come over in the spring. The weather here has been very cold and snowy. How has it been in your town?

I have good news - Lucy has had pups! I know that you want a dog, and your mother says I can bring one with me for you to meet. I have one in mind. Her name is Daisy, and she has big brown eyes just like you. I think you'll get along very well. See you soon!

Lots of love, Aunt Dorothy xxx

59

r	g	p	i	n	s
i	n	g	s	r	p
p	s	r	n	i	g
s	p	i	r	g	n
n	i	s	g	p	r
g	r	n	p	s	i

60

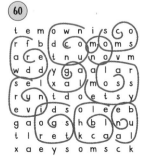

61

swim
jump
hurtle
depart
zoom
soar
spin
move
flee
glide

62

scarlet
crimson
yellow
maroon
purple
orange
lavender
saffron
violet

63

sea w a ter

sun s h ine

ord i n ary

rin g t one

lem o n ade

bir d c age

Washington DC

65

The answer is "insect"

66

1. I will meet you at the library at one o'clock.

2. I'm in trouble. The dog ate my homework!

67

anthem
betray
cotton
howled
impact
napkin
puppet
redone
seethe
wintry

70

1. You can take a horse to water, but you can't make it drink.
2. People who live in glass houses should not throw stones.
3. Too many cooks spoil the broth.
4. If it ain't broke, don't fix it.
5. Two wrongs don't make a right.
6. The early bird catches the worm.
7. Birds of a feather flock together.
8. A watched pot never boils.
9. When in Rome, do as the Romans do.
10. Two heads are better than one.
11. Honesty is the best policy.

72

P	O	O	D	L	E	S		
L		C		U		I		
E	V	E		C	O	R	G	I
A		A		K				C
D	A	N	E		S	H	O	E
E			H		O			B
D	I	N	G	O		U	S	E
	I		W		N			R
	B	U	L	L	D	O	G	

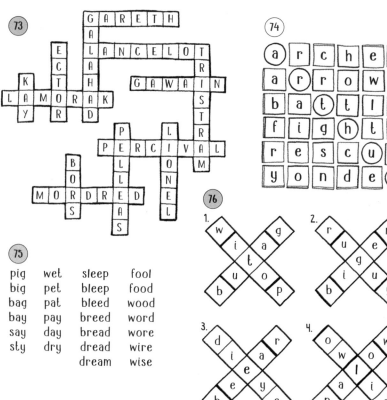

73

74

75

pig   wet   sleep   fool
big   pet   bleep   food
bag   pat   bleed   wood
bay   pay   breed   word
say   day   bread   wore
sty   dry   dread   wire
            dream   wise

76

77

goldfish

80

1. rare   4. serious
2. basic   5. green
3. pretty 6. jungle

81

d r a g o n f l y

83

cat

84

funny

85

1. ball
2. eye
3. cat
4. short
5. gardener

86

1. pig   6. goose
2. cow   7. rabbit
3. horse   8. chicken
4. sheep   9. turkey
5. goat

87

r eade r   w indo w

d ance d   m ediu m

g ivin g   h ealt h

c lassi c   e xpos e

b athtu b   s woop s

88

take
care
look
leap
try
win

89

F	R	E	E	Z	E	S	
I		G		E		K	
S	U	G	A	R		I	C	E
H			O		L		M
I	T	C	H		S	L	I	P
N		O		I			E
G	U	M		D	I	V	E	R
	E		L		E		O
	S	H	E	L	T	E	R

91

1. broom ....room.... table .... tale
2. knew ....new.... monkey .... money
3. sight ....sigh.... tear .... ear
4. when ....hen.... witch .... itch
5. gold ....old.... began .... bean
6. world ....word.... flair .... fair
7. reed ....red.... head .... had
8. clever ....lever.... score .... sore
9. three ....tree.... hedge .... edge
10. brain ....rain.... robot .... root

92

93

B	R	A	Z	I	L
C	A	N	A	D	A
F	R	A	N	C	E
T	U	R	K	E	Y
S	W	E	D	E	N
Z	A	M	B	I	A

First published in 2020 by Usborne Publishing Ltd, 83–85 Saffron Hill, London EC1N 8RT, England. usborne.com
Copyright © 2020 Usborne Publishing Ltd. The name Usborne and the devices ♀♔ are Trade Marks of Usborne Publishing Ltd.
All rights reserved. No part of this publication may be reproduced, stored in a retrieval system, or transmitted in any form or by
any means, electronic, mechanical, photocopying, recording or otherwise, without the prior permission of the publisher.
First published in America in 2020, UE, EDC, Tulsa, Oklahoma 74146 usbornebooksandmore.com. Printed in the UAE